Christmas Fun

From the
Library of
Marnie
Tegler

Scholastic Publications Ltd.,
10 Earlham Street, London WC2H 9RX, UK

Scholastic Inc.,
730 Broadway, New York, NY 10003, USA

Scholastic Canada Ltd.,
123 Newkirk Road, Richmond Hill,
Ontario L4C 3G5, Canada

Ashton Scholastic Pty. Ltd.,
P O Box 579, Gosford, New South Wales,
Australia

Ashton Scholastic Ltd.,
165 Marua Road, Panmure, Auckland 6,
New Zealand

First published by Scholastic Publications Ltd., 1989

Text copyright © Karen King, 1989
Illustrations copyright © Scholastic Publications Ltd., 1989

ISBN 0 590 76129 3

10 9 8 7 6 5 4 3 2 1

Printed in Hong Kong

Karen King

Christmas Fun

Illustrated by Karen Tushingham

Hippo Books
Scholastic Publications Limited
London

CONTENTS

Before you start

You will need a grown-up to help you with some of the things in this book. Make sure you get everything you need ready before you start and if you are using glue or paint, cover the table with newspaper first and put on an apron. Have fun but don't forget to tidy up when you've finished!

Christmas Tree

Make your own Christmas tree.

You will need
a thin branch of a tree with small twigs on it
a tin of silver paint and a paintbrush
a plant pot
a sheet of silver foil
some soil from the garden

What you have to do

1) Cover the plant pot with silver foil.

2) Fill the plant pot with soil and plant the branch in it.

3) Put some newspaper around the base of the tree, to protect the flowerpot and soil, then paint the tree silver.

4) When the paint is dry you can decorate your tree.

You can paint the tree gold or white, if you prefer, and cover the plant pot with Christmas or crepe paper.

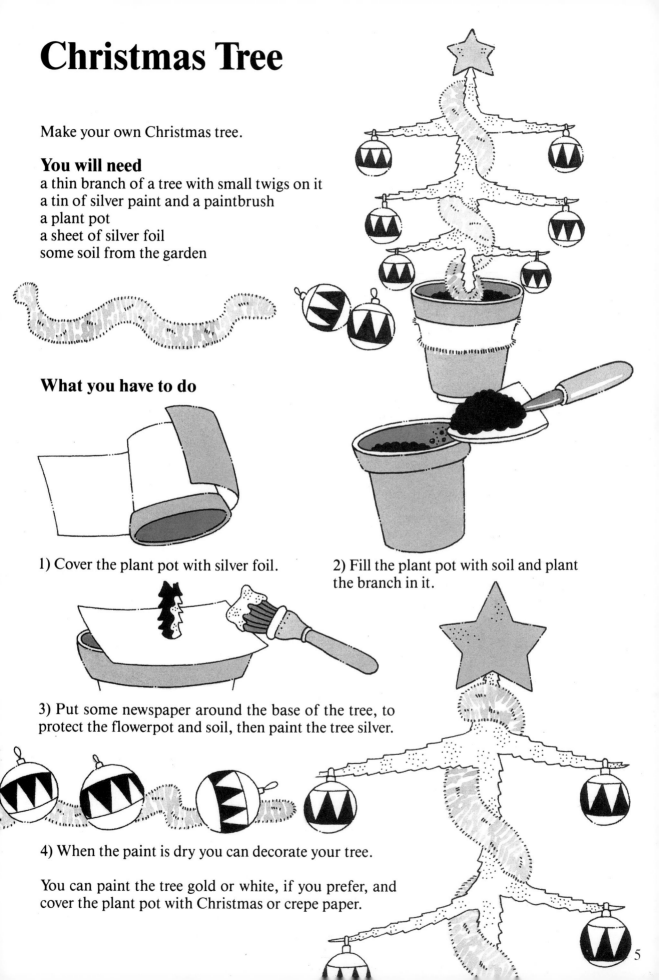

Santa Bauble

You will need
a ping pong ball or a white shatterproof bauble
cotton balls
piece of red crepe paper
glue, tape, a pencil and scissors
a blue and a red felt pen
thread or wool for hanging

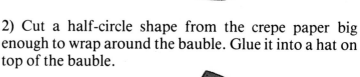

What you have to do
1) Draw on Santa's eyes, nose and mouth with the felt pen.

2) Cut a half-circle shape from the crepe paper big enough to wrap around the bauble. Glue it into a hat on top of the bauble.

3) Glue on some cotton balls for Santa's beard, and around his hat.
4) Tape a piece of thread or yarn to the back of Santa's hat so you can hang it from your tree.

Silver Bauble

You will need
an empty egg carton
silver foil
a needle and some thread
a bead with a hole in it

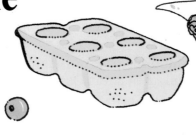

What you have to do
1) Cut out a segment from the egg carton.
2) Cover it with silver foil.
3) Pull thread through the hole in the bead, then up through the centre of the egg carton, so that the bead dangles in the middle. Before fastening off, leave a loop of thread at the top of the egg carton to hang the bead from the tree.

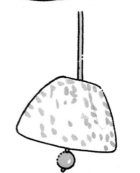

Paper Lantern

You will need
a small sheet of coloured paper
pencil and ruler
glue or tape and scissors

What you have to do
1) Rule a margin approx. 1 cm wide across the top and bottom of the paper.
2) Cut off a strip approx. 1 cm wide from one end. This is for the handle.
3) Fold the paper in half (as shown) and cut into strips from the middle to the margin.
4) Open out the paper, bend it around to form a lantern and paste or tape the sides together.
5) Join on the handle and hang it from your tree.

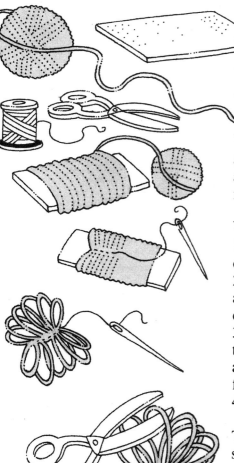

Pom-Pom Bauble

You will need
a ball of wool or yarn
a piece of cardboard approx. 5 by 10 cm
needle and thread and scissors

What you have to do
1) Wind the wool over and over the cardboard until it is completely covered.
2) Taking care not to sew into the cardboard, sew firmly along the centre of the wool on both sides of the cardboard, making sure you sew every strand together.
3) Carefully slip the wool off the cardboard and wind the sewing thread around the middle a few times. Leave a piece of thread to hang it from the tree, then knot firmly.
4) Cut open the ends to make your pom-pom bauble.

This looks very pretty if you can make it with gold or silver wool.

Christmas Templates

Trace these shapes onto stiff cardboard and use as templates for your Christmas cards or decorations. Cut out the shapes from silver foil or coloured shiny wrapping paper and hang them on your tree.

Stained-Glass Window Bauble

Use your Christmas Templates to make this pretty bauble.

You will need

black bristol board
coloured tissue paper or butcher paper
felt tip pens and a pencil
scissors, glue, needle and black thread

What you have to do

1) Draw around the template onto black bristol board and cut it out. Cut out the middle of the bristol board, leaving a margin of about 12 mm.

2) Draw around the template onto the tissue paper, cut it out and stick it onto the black bristol board. If you are using butcher paper, colour in the shape on both sides with your felt tip pens, cut it out and stick it onto the black bristol board.

3) Make a hole in the top of the black bristol board with a needle and slip through some black thread to hang the bauble from the tree. Be sure to hang it near the Christmas tree lights to make the colours glow.

More Decorations

There are lots of other decorations you can make. Try painting fir cones with silver, gold or white paint. Or painting broken egg shells, brushing on some glue and sprinkling on glitter.

You could make some little presents to hang from the tree by wrapping up matchboxes and other small items in Christmas paper. Wrap up differently shaped things like thread spools and pencils for an unusual effect. You can dress up the parcels with ribbon or little bows. Maybe you have some scraps of shiny coloured foil paper you could use to wrap the parcels up.

Make tiny stockings out of scrap material, fill them with candies and sew on a loop of yarn to hang from the tree. You can decorate them by gluing on some cotton balls, if you like.

To hang baubles from a tree you open a paper clip into an S shape and stick one hook through the bauble, and the other over the branch.

Puzzle Page

Spot the Difference

Look carefully and see if you can spot the eight differences between these two pictures.

The Maze

Rudolph is hurrying to help Santa deliver the presents. Can you help him find his way through the wood to Santa's sleigh?

Christmas Wreath

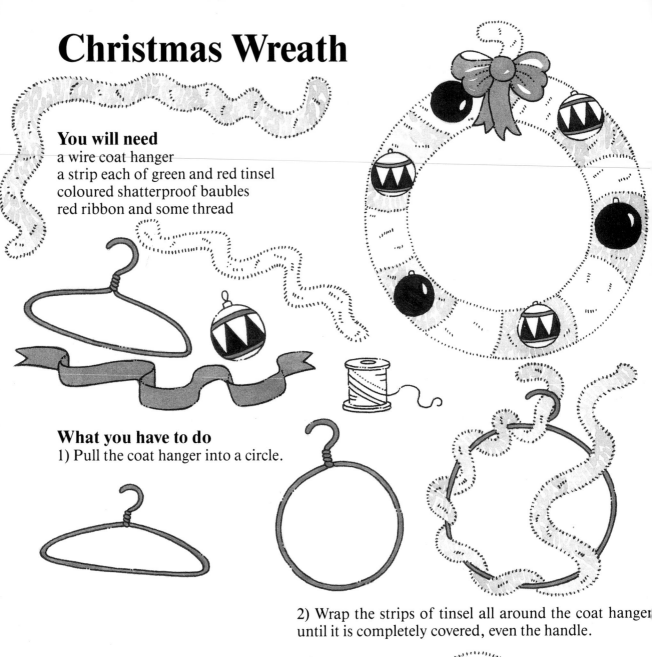

You will need
a wire coat hanger
a strip each of green and red tinsel
coloured shatterproof baubles
red ribbon and some thread

What you have to do
1) Pull the coat hanger into a circle.

2) Wrap the strips of tinsel all around the coat hanger until it is completely covered, even the handle.

3) Slip thread through the baubles and tie them onto the wreath to decorate it.
4) Tie the red ribbon into a big bow around the handle.

Now your Christmas wreath is ready to hang on the wall.

Christmas Angel

You can put this angel on top of the tree or use it as a table decoration.

You will need

a piece of white, silver or gold paper
silver foil
a small white, silver or gold shatterproof bauble
two toothpicks
glue, tape, pencil and scissors

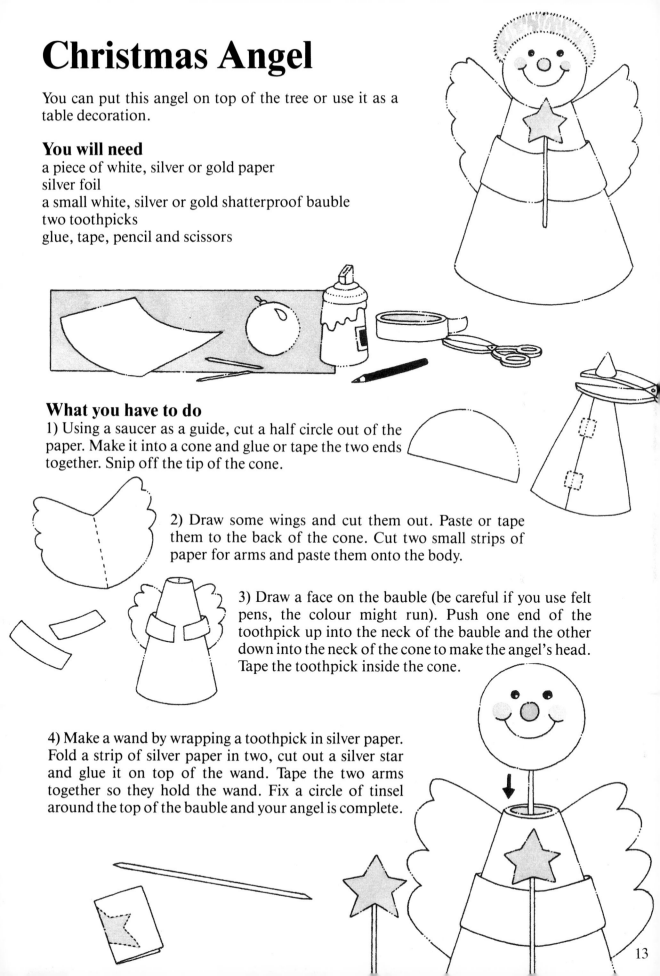

What you have to do

1) Using a saucer as a guide, cut a half circle out of the paper. Make it into a cone and glue or tape the two ends together. Snip off the tip of the cone.

2) Draw some wings and cut them out. Paste or tape them to the back of the cone. Cut two small strips of paper for arms and paste them onto the body.

3) Draw a face on the bauble (be careful if you use felt pens, the colour might run). Push one end of the toothpick up into the neck of the bauble and the other down into the neck of the cone to make the angel's head. Tape the toothpick inside the cone.

4) Make a wand by wrapping a toothpick in silver paper. Fold a strip of silver paper in two, cut out a silver star and glue it on top of the wand. Tape the two arms together so they hold the wand. Fix a circle of tinsel around the top of the bauble and your angel is complete.

Bows

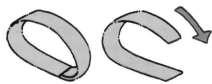

Bows add a nice touch to any present. Make a pretty bow by cutting out 4 x 15 cm strips of narrow ribbon. Fold each strip in half and glue the ends together.

Glue the inside of each loop to stick it together in the middle.

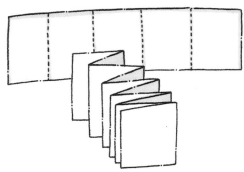

Then glue the back of the loops and stick them onto each other, criss-cross fashion. Staple them in the middle. You can cover the staple by rolling up a small piece of ribbon and gluing it over it.

Christmas Cut-Outs

You can decorate a present wrapped up in plain paper by gluing on a cut-out decoration, like this angel one. You will need a long strip of paper. Fold it backwards and forwards, as in this diagram.

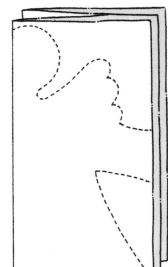

Draw half of an angel, making sure that the angel's wings and hem of her dress reach to the folded edges. Cut around the outline, as shown by the dotted line.

Open out the paper and glue your row of angels onto a present.

Cut-Out Christmas Cards

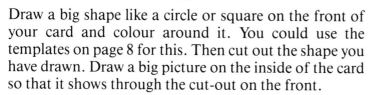

Draw a big shape like a circle or square on the front of your card and colour around it. You could use the templates on page 8 for this. Then cut out the shape you have drawn. Draw a big picture on the inside of the card so that it shows through the cut-out on the front.

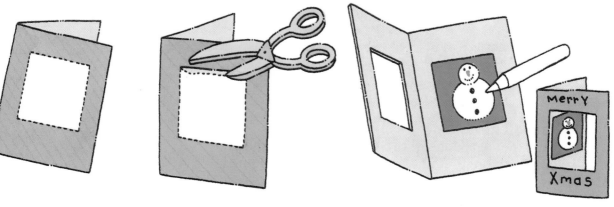

Experiment with cut-outs and see how many different cards you can make. Draw a picture of three baubles on the front of your card. Carefully cut out the middle bauble. Draw a picture on the inside of the card, so that it shows through the cut-out. Then write a message on the front and inside the card.

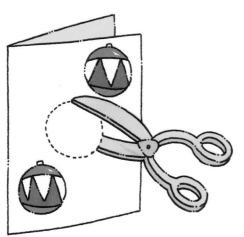

Christmas Card Mobiles

A good way to display your Christmas cards is to hang them on a mobile.

You will need
a wire coat hanger
some tinsel
paper clips
Christmas cards

What you have to do

1) Cover the coat hanger with tinsel, including the hook. It looks very pretty if you use two differently coloured strips of tinsel, like red and silver.

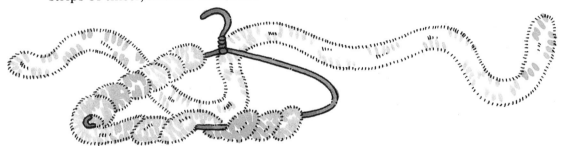

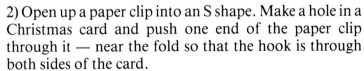

2) Open up a paper clip into an S shape. Make a hole in a Christmas card and push one end of the paper clip through it — near the fold so that the hook is through both sides of the card.

3) Put the other end of the paper clip over the coat hanger, then press it together so it doesn't fall off. You can hang lots of cards over the hanger in this way.

You can hook the coat hanger onto a shelf or hang it from the ceiling.

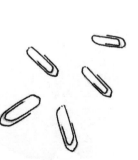

Fan Mobile

You will need
a clothes peg
some paint
a small piece of ribbon or yarn

What you have to do

1) Paint the peg and leave it to dry.

2) Thread the yarn or ribbon through the peg, tying with a bow at the top.

3) Peg several cards together, spreading them out in a fan shape.

4) Hang the peg from the wall by putting a drawing pin in the bow.

Open-the-Door Card

For this you need a long, rectangular piece of bristol board or paper, at least 31 cm by 15 cm. Measure the board into three equal sections

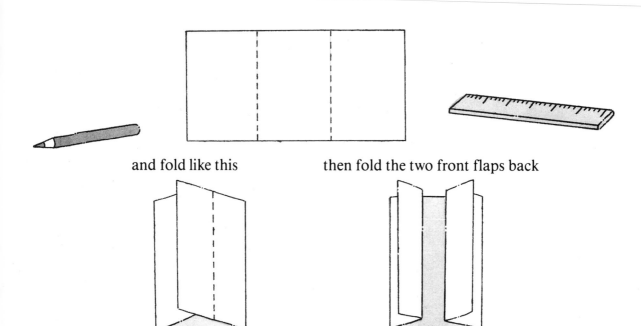

and fold like this   then fold the two front flaps back

Open out the bristol board. On the two outside flaps draw an angel, in the centre draw Baby Jesus in the crib. On one side of Baby Jesus draw Mary, on the other side draw Joseph.

Fold the bristol board so that you can't see the picture of the crib until the angels open the doors.
See if you can think of another design for this idea.

Christmas Word Search

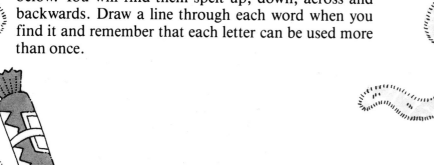

See if you can find the following words in the square below. You will find them spelt up, down, across and backwards. Draw a line through each word when you find it and remember that each letter can be used more than once.

```
A C H R I S T M A S T R E E S P
O R B C C T U L U A V O O N Y A
V A Q O N H R D N L H N S F O P
R C L T B G K K W E X M T Q T E
A K D D R I E S L I N G E I H R
C E M E W L Y T S P J Q E K L H
S R X C J E S U S M T K W W Q A
E S I O M O S D R A C R S Y P T
I B M R M E U N R W K J F L G S
P R M A D S G B C A N D L E S S
E V S T N E S E R P M L H S Y L
C D J I L Y R R E M A C M N K O
N X M O A S R K L B T E O I P R
I S A N T A C L A U S M B T V A
M D C S X Q R F S E I T R A P C
```

Up	Down	Across	Backwards
mince pies	crackers	Santa Claus	merry
lights	paper hats	Jesus	parties
sweets	turkey	candles	cards
toys	decorations	Christmas tree	presents
carols			
tinsel			

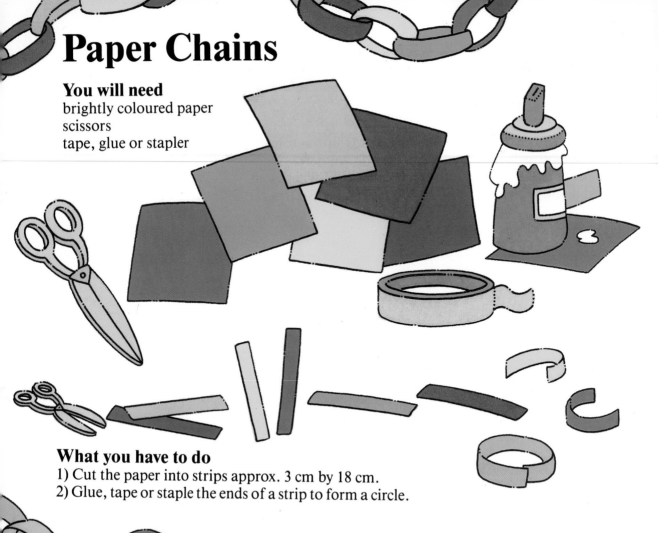

Paper Chains

You will need
brightly coloured paper
scissors
tape, glue or stapler

What you have to do
1) Cut the paper into strips approx. 3 cm by 18 cm.
2) Glue, tape or staple the ends of a strip to form a circle.

3) Loop another strip through the circle you have just made and join the ends.
4) Keep looping the strips like this until you have made your chain as long as you need it. You can make a pretty effect by doing chains in all different colours, or alternating two colours like red and white.

Lacy Streamers

You will need
strips of crepe paper about 50 cm long and 10 cm wide
(length can vary).

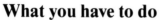
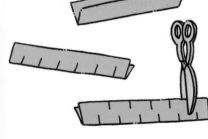

What you have to do
1) Fold a strip of paper in half, lengthwise.
2) Carefully cut along the folded edge of the paper, making strips of approx. 2 cm wide. Don't cut right to the opposite edge.
3) Now cut strips along the other side, alternating between the first strips. Take care that you don't cut into the same strip.
4) When you have finished, carefully spread out the paper. Don't pull too hard or you will rip it.

You can join several streamers of different colours together to make a long colourful one.

Square Lantern

You can use coloured tissue paper, crepe paper or shiny coloured foil wrapping paper to make this pretty lantern.

You will need

2 squares of coloured paper, each measuring 15 cm
a strip of the same paper measuring 5 cm by 8 cm
scissors, tape, glue and thread

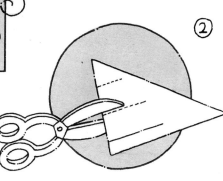

What you have to do

1) Fold one of the squares of paper into a triangle. Then fold it over again to make a smaller triangle (diagram 1).

2) Cut two slits, about 2.5 cm apart, into one of the smaller, folded sides of the triangle, cutting towards the other folded side but not right up to it.

3) Now turn the triangle around and cut two slits into the other folded side, cutting between the slits you have just made from the other side (diagram 2).

4) Carefully unfold the triangle and open it out into a square again (diagram 3).

5) Repeat from steps 1 to 4, with the other square of paper.

6) Glue both squares together at each corner (diagram 4).

7) Now take the small strip of paper and cut thin strips along one edge, to fringe it. Roll it up and staple it together at the top (diagram 5).

8) Make a little slit in the middle of the bottom lantern and glue or staple the rolled up piece in the split, so that it dangles from the lantern (diagram 6).

9) Tape some thread onto the middle of the top square of the lantern to hang it up.

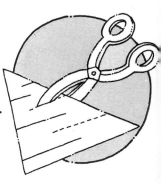

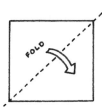

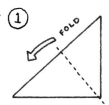

Christmas snowscene

This pretty snowscene is very simple to make and will make a lovely present for someone special.

You will need
an assortment of small plastic figures, you could use Christmas cake decorations
a small glass jar with a screw-on lid (like a honey jar)
a vial of Christmas snow glitter. If you haven't any snow glitter you can use desiccated coconut and white vinegar.
strong waterproof glue
eyebrow tweezers

What you have to do
1) Glue the bottom of one of the figures and place it on the bottom of the jar. Use the eyebrow tweezers to help set the figure in place.

2) Glue the other figures inside the jar and leave them to dry overnight so that the glue can set.

3) When the figures are glued firmly, pour snow glitter into the jar and fill it with water. Or put in two heaped spoonfuls of desiccated coconut and fill the jar with white vinegar.

4) Glue around the rim of the jar and screw the lid on tight.
5) Now shake the jar and watch the snow fall!

Finger Puppets

Make a family of finger puppets for your little brother or sister or a friend.

You will need
piece of stiff paper and a pencil
scraps of material or felt
scraps of yarn or wool
pins, needle and thread
glue

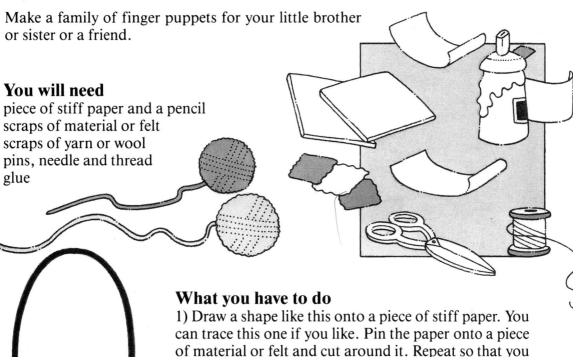

What you have to do
1) Draw a shape like this onto a piece of stiff paper. You can trace this one if you like. Pin the paper onto a piece of material or felt and cut around it. Repeat so that you have two shapes.

2) Put the right sides of the shapes together and sew around the edges, leaving a gap at the bottom to put your finger through.

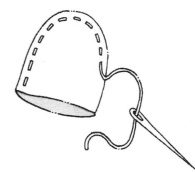

3) Turn the puppet right way out. Cut out some eyes, nose and mouth from material or paper and glue them on. Glue on some yarn for hair.

Santa Sleigh Game

Play this game with your friends. You will need a dice and counters or buttons for 2-4 players. Players take turns to throw the dice. See what number the dice lands on and move forward that many places. If you land on a square with a message on you must obey it. The first one to get Santa home is the winner.

CAN'T FIND RUDOLPH, MISS A TURN... **1**

13

SHORT CUT TO JAPAN, GO TO NUMBER 21... **17**

16

15

SLEIGH GETS STUCK IN SNOW, NEED A **6** TO CONTINUE... **14**

18

19

STOP FOR A MINCE PIE, MISS A TURN... **20**

21

36

35

SHORT CUT TO AMERICA, GO TO NUMBER 40... **34**

PRESENTS FALL OUT OF SACK, MISS A TURN... **33**

A CHILD SEES YOU, MISS A TURN... **37**

38

39

MISSED OUT MEXICO! GO BACK TO NUMBER 35... **40**

Christmas Crib
Turn to page 29 to find out how to make your Christmas Crib

Jumping Santa
Turn to page 29 to find out how to make your Jumping
Santa

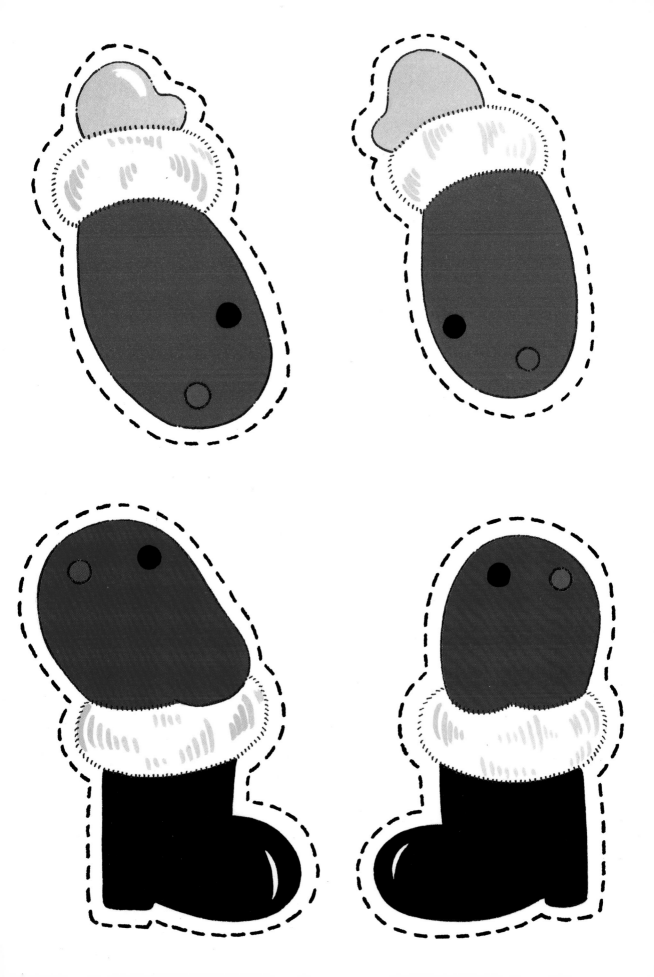

Snowman On Ice

You will need

a cardboard tube from a toilet roll
cotton wool
glue
coloured paper and scissors
piece of material for a scarf
square of cardboard
silver foil

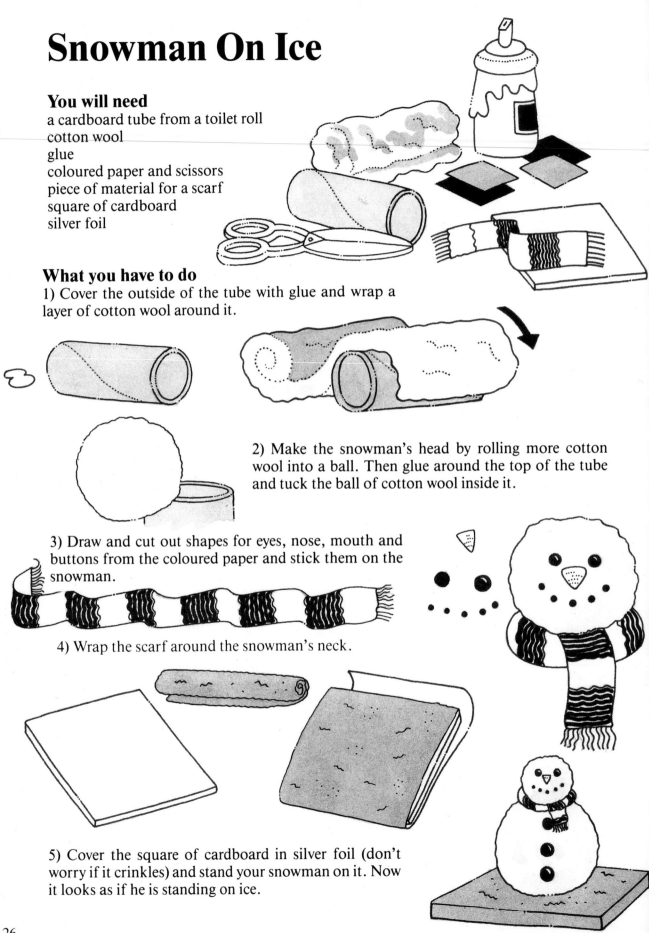

What you have to do

1) Cover the outside of the tube with glue and wrap a layer of cotton wool around it.

2) Make the snowman's head by rolling more cotton wool into a ball. Then glue around the top of the tube and tuck the ball of cotton wool inside it.

3) Draw and cut out shapes for eyes, nose, mouth and buttons from the coloured paper and stick them on the snowman.

4) Wrap the scarf around the snowman's neck.

5) Cover the square of cardboard in silver foil (don't worry if it crinkles) and stand your snowman on it. Now it looks as if he is standing on ice.

Santa Straws

Trace this picture of Santa onto some stiff white paper or bristol board, colour it and cut it out.

Then make two slits where the black lines are, making two holes big enough to put drinking straws through. You may need a grown-up to help you do this. Push the straws through the black lines, as in the diagram. Try making up your own pictures too; you could do a different design for each guest.

Puzzle Page

Word ladder

Can you change the word ROCK into the word SAND in four turns? You can only alter one letter at a time and you must make a proper word every time, like in this example:

Change CARD to GAME   Now change ROCK to SAND

CARD   ROCK
CARE   - - - -
CAME   - - - -
GAME   - - - -
                SAND

Balloon Mix-up

These children have got their balloons mixed up. Can you untangle the strings and see which balloon belongs to which child?

How To Make Your Christmas Crib

You will need

a shoe box with a lid
scissors, stapler and felt tip pens or paints
the Christmas crib figures provided in the centre of this book

What you have to do

1) To make the stable, cut off the rim of the shoe box lid, then colour the lid and box brown. Colour it inside and out.
2) Lie the shoe box on its side, fold the lid in half, crease it down the middle then open it out again. Staple it to the box, overlapping slightly, as in the diagram. Then make a small hole in the centre of the lid at the front to hang your star.
3) Cut out the Christmas crib figures. Make a hole in the top of the star. Open up a paper clip and put one end through the hole in the star and the other end through the hole in the roof of the stable.
4) Now arrange your figures around your Christmas crib.

How To Make Your Jumping Santa

You will need

the Santa shapes provided in the centre of this book
four split-pin paper fasteners
string or yarn

What you have to do

1) Cut out the Santa shapes.
2) Make holes in all the black dots and brown dots. Join the arms and legs to the body by pushing split pins through the black holes.
3) Cut two pieces of string or yarn about 28 cm long. Thread a piece of yarn through the small holes on the arms and knot it at the back of the Santa. Do the same with the legs.
4) Cut another piece of string about 31 cm long and loosely knot it around the string across the arms, then bring it down and loosely tie around the string across the legs (see diagram).
5) Pull the string and watch your Santa jump for joy!

Sock Puppet

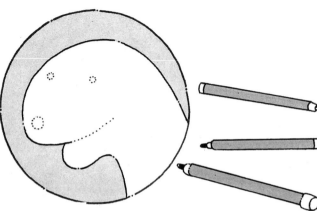

You will need

an old sock
2 buttons and odd scraps of material
glue and scissors
felt pen

What you have to do

1) Put the sock on your hand so that the heel is under the palm of your hand.
2) Use the felt pen to mark where you want the eyes, nose and mouth.

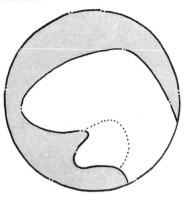

3) Take the sock off your hand and sew on the buttons for eyes.

4) Cut out shapes for the nose and mouth from the scrap material and glue them onto the sock to make a face.

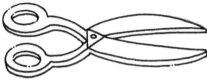

Make a few sock puppets and put on a puppet show!

Pet's Christmas Stocking

Give your pet a treat!

You will need

a piece of thick cardboard about 40 cm long and 23 cm wide
a ladies' nylon stocking or a pair of tights
pencil, paints or crayons and scissors

What you have to do

1) Draw a shape like this on your piece of cardboard. You can do a dog's or cat's head. Paint or crayon it.

2) Gently pull the stocking over the cardboard and roll it down at the top. If you are using an old pair of tights, cut the top and one of the legs off, then pull that over the cardboard, rolling it down at the top.

3) Put in a couple of treats like pet toys or biscuits and give it to your dog or cat on Christmas Day.

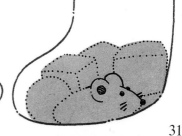

Fancy-Dress Fun

Ask a grown-up to help you make one of these costumes if you've been invited to a Fancy-Dress party this Christmas.

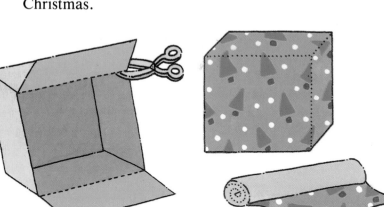

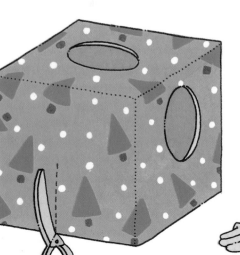

Christmas Present

Cut out the bottom of a big box and cover it with Christmas paper. Then cut out a hole in the top of it, big enough to put your head through, and a hole in each side to put your arms through.

Cut up the middle of the back of the box, to make it easier to put on. Put your arms through the holes in the side of the box, ask someone to tape it up at the back and tie a ribbon around the middle. Now you're a walking Christmas present!

Star

Be the star of the party!
Cut two big stars out of cardboard and paint them yellow. Make a hole in both stars, as shown, and thread some string through the holes in one of the stars.

Put on some yellow tights and a yellow sweater. Ask someone to help you tie the stars on so that one is at the back and one at the front.
You could tie some sparkly tinsel on your shoes and in your hair, too.

Christmas Cookery

These sweets can make a lovely present if they are packed prettily.

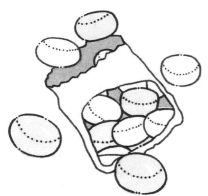

Chocolate Marshmallows

You will need
a packet of marshmallows
a bar of baker's chocolate
a packet of smarties
paper candy cups
toothpicks

What you have to do
1) Ask a grown-up to melt the chocolate for you.
2) Spear a marshmallow with a toothpick and roll it in the melted chocolate.
3) Put a smartie on top and leave on a tray until firm.
4) Put each marshmallow in a candy cup.

Peppermint Creams

You will need

750 ml of icing sugar
the white of a small egg
5 drops of peppermint flavouring

a mixing bowl
paper candy cups
an egg cup

What you have to do

1) Put the icing sugar into a mixing bowl. Add the peppermint flavouring and the egg white and stir until it forms a very thick paste. If the mixture is still sticky, add a bit more icing sugar.

2) Coat a board or table top with icing sugar and put the mixture on it. Knead it well until firm and dry then roll it out, to about 1 cm thick.

3) Use an egg cup to cut out the peppermint creams, put them in the cups and leave them in the fridge to set.

Candy Basket

Pack your candies into a little basket made out of an empty margarine container. Wash the container and cover it with silver foil. Make a handle for the basket by rolling up several flat layers of silver foil, then tape it to the container. Put a paper doily inside, arranging the frilly edge around the top, and put in your candies.

Stocking Fillers

Slip these little presents into someone's stocking!

Thread-Spool Rabbit

You will need
an empty thread spool
white cardboard and tracing paper
scissors and glue
pencil and crayons

What you have to do
1) Trace the head and body of this rabbit onto the cardboard and colour them in.
2) Glue the rabbit's head to one end of the spool, and the body to the other end.

You could draw the heads and bodies of other animals like a cat or dog and make lots of pets.

Pocket Puzzle

You will need
the lid of a screw-on jar with cardboard inside (like a coffee lid)
a piece of white cardboard
2 silver balls (like the ones used for decorating cakes)
plastic wrap
pencil, crayons and scissors

What you have to do
1) Remove the cardboard lining from the lid of the jar and draw around it onto the piece of white cardboard.
2) Cut out the circle of cardboard and draw a face on it.
3) Using the point of your pencil, punch two holes where the eyes should be.
4) Put the cardboard into the jar lid and put the two silver balls inside.
5) Cover with plastic wrap, stretching it tightly over the top and taping it firmly at the back of the lid.
6) Now shake the puzzle and see if you can get the two balls to rest on the eyes.

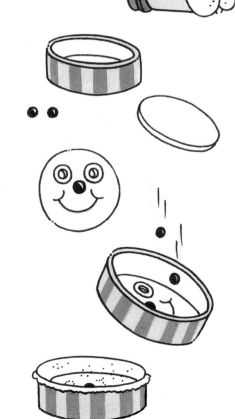

Santa's Workshop

All the elves are busy making toys in Santa's workshop.
Colour this picture carefully with your paints or
crayons. Then see if you can count how many elves,
teddies and cars there are.

Puzzle page

Whose Present Is It?

Can you unscramble these names to find out who the presents belong to?

1) thyomit

2) retpe

3) nassu

4) damyn

5) vadid

6) nidal

Which Two Are The Same?

These six angels all look the same but only two are identical. Can you spot the matching pair?

38

Party Balloons

Make some balloon people for your party! Everyone can take one home on a string.

You will need
a packet of balloons
squares of coloured gummed paper
yarn and glue

What you have to do
1) Ask a grown-up to blow the balloons up, taking care not to blow them up too big or they will burst.
2) Draw some eyes, nose and mouth shapes on the coloured gummed paper. Cut them out and stick them onto the balloons, making a funny face.
3) Now make some hair out of the yarn and stick it on the balloons.

See how many funny balloon faces you can make!

Sewing Box

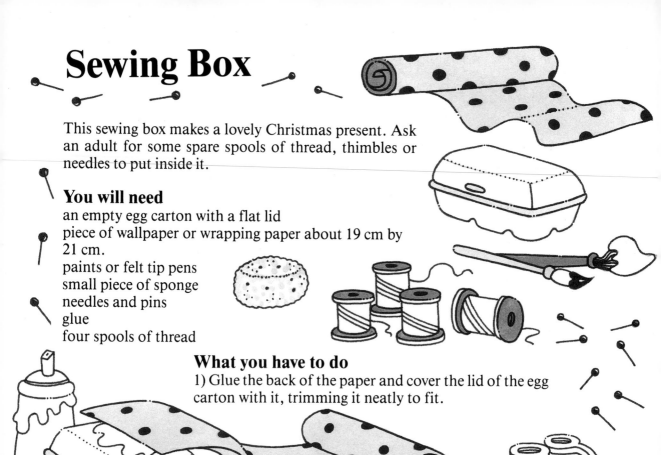

This sewing box makes a lovely Christmas present. Ask an adult for some spare spools of thread, thimbles or needles to put inside it.

You will need

an empty egg carton with a flat lid
piece of wallpaper or wrapping paper about 19 cm by 21 cm.
paints or felt tip pens
small piece of sponge
needles and pins
glue
four spools of thread

What you have to do

1) Glue the back of the paper and cover the lid of the egg carton with it, trimming it neatly to fit.

2) Colour the bottom of the egg carton with your paints or felt tip pens.

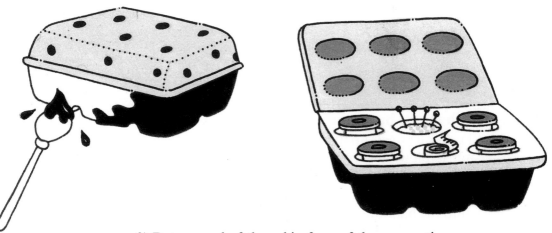

3) Put a spool of thread in four of the egg sections.
4) Put the piece of sponge in another section and stick in a couple of needles and pins.
5) Put a thimble or rolled up tape measure in the last section.

Santa Claus Cracker

You will need

the cardboard tube from a toilet roll
red crepe paper
white paper and felt tip pens
scissors, thread, glue or sticky tape
a small gift or packet of candies

What you have to do

1) Cut a square of crepe paper about 8 cm bigger than the cardboard tube.

2) Place the cardboard tube on the paper. Then put a small gift or packet of candies in the tube.

3) Roll the paper around the tube. Tie a piece of thread around each end of the wrapped tube. Fringe the ends.

4) Draw Santa's head and hands on the white paper. Colour them in. Cut them out and glue or tape them onto the cracker. Draw on some buttons too.

You could also write a joke on a piece of paper and put it in the cracker.

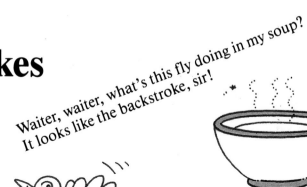

Jokes

What holds the sun up in the sky?
The sunbeams!

Waiter, waiter, what's this fly doing in my soup?
It looks like the backstroke, sir!

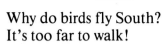

Why do birds fly South?
It's too far to walk!

What kind of bow can't be tied?
A rainbow!

What's the difference between an elephant and a biscuit?
You can't dip an elephant in your tea!

What's green and goes boing, boing?
A spring cabbage!

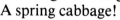

Party Invites

Half blow up some balloons. Write the details of your party on each one. Let the balloons down, put them in envelopes and send them to your friends. Tell them to blow up the balloons and they can read your message.

Christmas Tree Place Cards

You will need

a strip of green paper (about 20 cm by 12 cm), or white paper and a green crayon
pencil, scissors and glue

What you have to do

1) Fold the paper backwards and forwards, making five folds all together (diagram 1).

①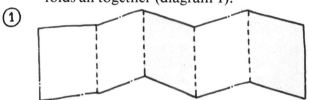

②

2) Draw half of a Christmas tree on the top layer of paper, making sure the branches reach right up to the folded edge (diagram 2).

3) Cut around the outline, through all the layers, as shown by the dotted line.

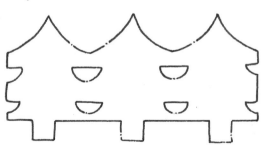

③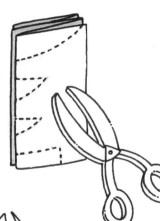

4) You will have three trees. If you are using white paper, colour the trees in green. Then fold the two side trees back, behind the middle tree, and glue their end halves together so that the middle tree stands up (diagram 3).

5) Put a tree by each plate and write the name of your guest on the front.

Puzzle Page

Join The Dots

Can you guess what present this little elf has had for Christmas? Join the dots and see if you guessed right!

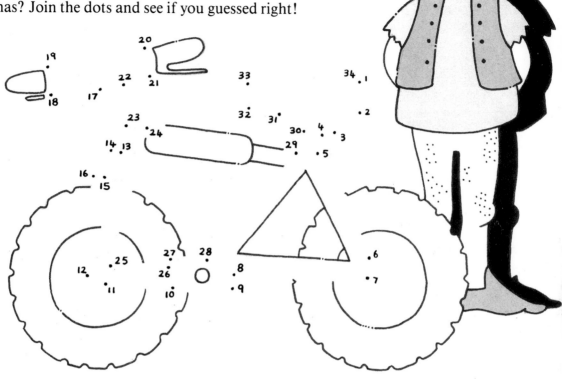

Pair Them Up!

Can you pair these things up to make six other words?

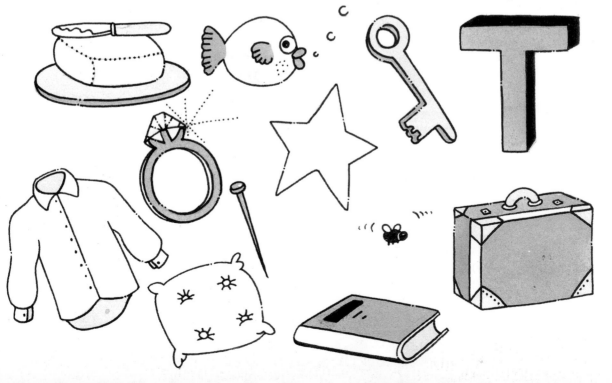

Crib Crossword

How well do you know the Christmas story? See if you can answer the questions about the Nativity to fill in the clues to this crossword.

Clues

Across

1) The shepherds were looking after their – – – – – when the angel came to them.

5) Jesus was born in a little town called – – – – – – – – –.

7) Mary rode on a – – – – – –.

9) God sent an angel to tell Mary she was having a – – – –.

10) Two animals were in the stable; one was an – –.

11) Mary called her baby – – – – –.

12) Jesus was the Son of – – –.

13) – – – – – Wise Men followed the Star.

15) The Wise Men brought gifts of gold, frankincense and – – – – – to Baby Jesus.

Down

2) King – – – – – was ruling when Jesus was born.

3) Jesus was born in a – – – – – – because all the inns were full.

4) Mary's husband was called – – – – – –.

6) Jesus's crib was a – – – – – –.

8) The Wise Men saw a star shining in the – – – –.

14) Mary and Joseph slept on a bed of – – –.

Wrap It Up

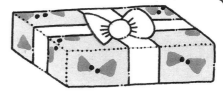

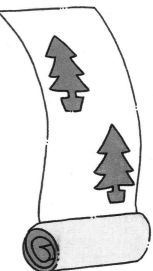

Make your Christmas presents look special. Use several sheets of coloured crepe paper. Wrap the presents up in one colour and cut a long strip off a different coloured sheet to wrap around in a bow.

Or you could use rolls of white shelf paper and make your own design on them. You can do this very easily by using the Christmas templates on page 8. Trace the template you want to use onto thick cardboard. Then cover one side of the cardboard with thick poster paint. Place the painted side onto the paper and press. Repeat all over the paper. You could use all the templates and make lots of different designs.

Fancy Wraps

There are lots of clever ways you can wrap your presents up to disguise the contents.

Cracker
A long, thin parcel can be disguised as a cracker. You will need a piece of paper longer than the present. Lie the present on the paper and roll the paper around it, taping it securely. Then tie some cord or string around both ends to make it look like a cracker. Open up the ends and fringe them.

Dice
Cover a square-box-shaped present with plain paper. Cut out several circles from paper of another colour. Stick them on the box as spots, one spot on one side, two on another etc. to make it look like a dice.

Candle
A tall, cylinder-shaped present like a bottle of bubble bath can be disguised as a candle. First cover the present with plain paper. Then cut out a long, thin strip of a contrasting colour paper. Glue it spiral-fashion, from the bottom to the top of the cylinder. Make a flame shape out of stiff paper and colour it in red and yellow. Tape this to the top of the cylinder to complete your candle.

Jewellery

You will need

750 mL of plain flour
250 mL of salt and some water
pastry cutters
mixing bowl, rolling pin, and flour for rolling out
poster paints, glue and a plastic knife
safety pins, small curtain rings and ribbon

What you have to do

1) Put the flour and salt into a mixing bowl and mix well. Then slowly add the water to make a very stiff paste. This is your modelling dough.
2) Put the dough onto a floured board and roll it out.
3) Using the pastry cutter, cut out some shapes. You can then 'draw' on the dough to make a face etc. or mould it into your own design.

4) You can make brooches by pushing a safety pin into the back of the dough shape – make sure you put it in the right way! Or make pendants by pressing a curtain ring into the top of a shape to hang on a piece of ribbon.

5) Now place the jewellery on a floured baking tray. Then, ask a grown-up to put it in the oven on a very low heat (120°C or 250°F) to bake for an hour.
6) When the dough is cool, you can paint it. Mix the poster paints with a bit of glue so that it sticks.

Presents with Jars

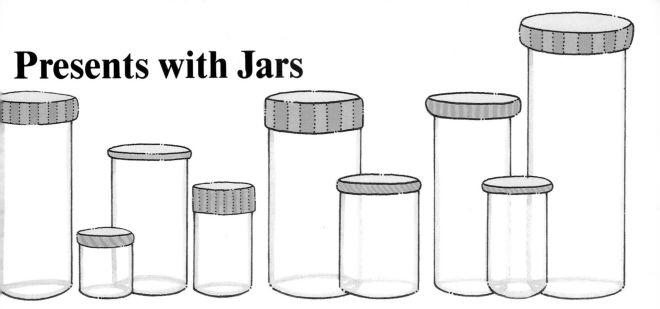

Jars can turn simple things into presents. They can be any shape or size, even a simple jam jar.

Get a clean jar and fill it with bath crystals. You can buy these very cheaply from a drugstore. Tie a pretty bow around the jar and paint the lid to match.

Fill a clean jar with toffees or candies. Paint the lid. Stick some Christmas stickers around the jar.

Get a small, unusually shaped jar. You don't need the lid. Put in a pen, pencil, rubber and ruler. Now you have an unusual pen holder to give someone.

Fill a jar with coloured cotton balls and put some tissue or soft material over the top of it, instead of a lid. Hold in place with an elastic band.

Answers

p.11

Spot the difference

The maze
C is the correct path.

p.28

Word ladder
ROCK
SOCK
SACK
SANK
SAND

Balloon mix-up
Balloon A belongs to child 3.
Balloon B belongs to child 1.
Balloon C belongs to child 4.
Balloon D belongs to child 2.

p. 37

Santa's workshop
There are 10 elves, 8 cars and 12 teddies.

p.38

Whose present is it?
1) Timothy
2) Peter
3) Susan
4) Mandy
5) David
6) Linda

p.19

Christmas word search

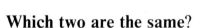

Which two are the same?
Angels 2 and 5 are identical.

p.43

Join the dots
It is a bicycle.

Pair them up!
keyring
starfish
butterfly
bookcase
pincushion
T-shirt

p.44

Crib crossword

Across	Down
1) sheep	2) Herod
5) Bethlehem	3) stable
7) donkey	4) Joseph
9) baby	6) manger
10) ox	8) East
11) Jesus	14) hay
12) God	
13) three	
15) myrrh	